PERIOD.

WRITTEN & ILLUSTRATED
BY NATALIE BYRNE

B \ T \ H

B \ T \ H

First published in 2018 by Break the Habit Press
www.breakthehabitpress.com
www.nat-b.com

A CIP catalogue record for this book is available from the British Library

978-1-9998941-1-5

Printed and bound in Great Britain by Page Bros (Norwich) Ltd

For my mum and grandma.

CONTENTS

Introduction   I

Chapter One: Our Bodies   1
On the Outside   5
On the Inside   29

Chapter Two: The Menstrual Cycle   47
Menstruation Phase   52
Follicular Phase   54
Ovulation Phase   56
Luteal Phase   58
Hormones   62
Menopause   64
Track Yours   66

Chapter Three: Period Products   69
Pads   74
Tampons   88
Menstrual Cups   102
Period Underwear   118
Period Poverty   130
Busting Period Product Myths   132

Chapter Four: Healthy Down There   137

Period Blood   140
Irregular Periods   144
Heavy Periods   146
Discharge   152
Common Problems   158

Chapter Five: Feeling Good   167

Common Symptoms of PMS   170
Cramps   174
Bloating   176
Acne   178
Sore Boobs   186
Food   190
Exercise   192
Mood Changes   194
Mental Health   196

Chapter Six: Bloody History   201

Ancient Egyptians, Greeks and Romans   204
Medieval Europeans   201

Afterword   217

Thank Yous
Sponsors

WE ACKNOWLEDGE:

♡ THAT ALL BODIES ARE UNIQUE
  AND DIFFERENT

♡ THAT ALL ADVICE IS SUBJECTIVE
  AND MIGHT NOT WORK FOR YOU

♡ THAT HAVING A PERIOD DOESN'T
  DETERMINE YOUR GENDER

THIS BOOK IS NOT ABOUT
A PERIOD OF TIME.

NOR IS IT ABOUT
PUNCTUATION.

THIS BOOK IS ABOUT MENSTRUATION.

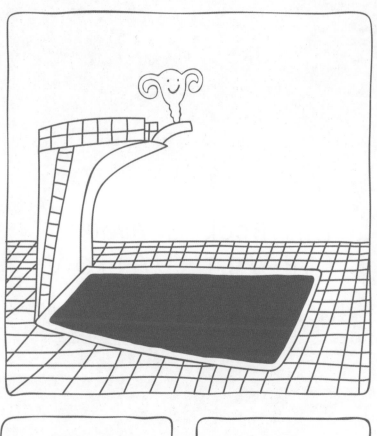

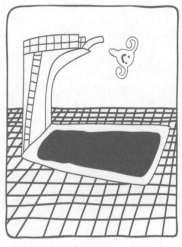

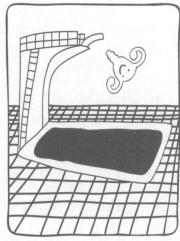

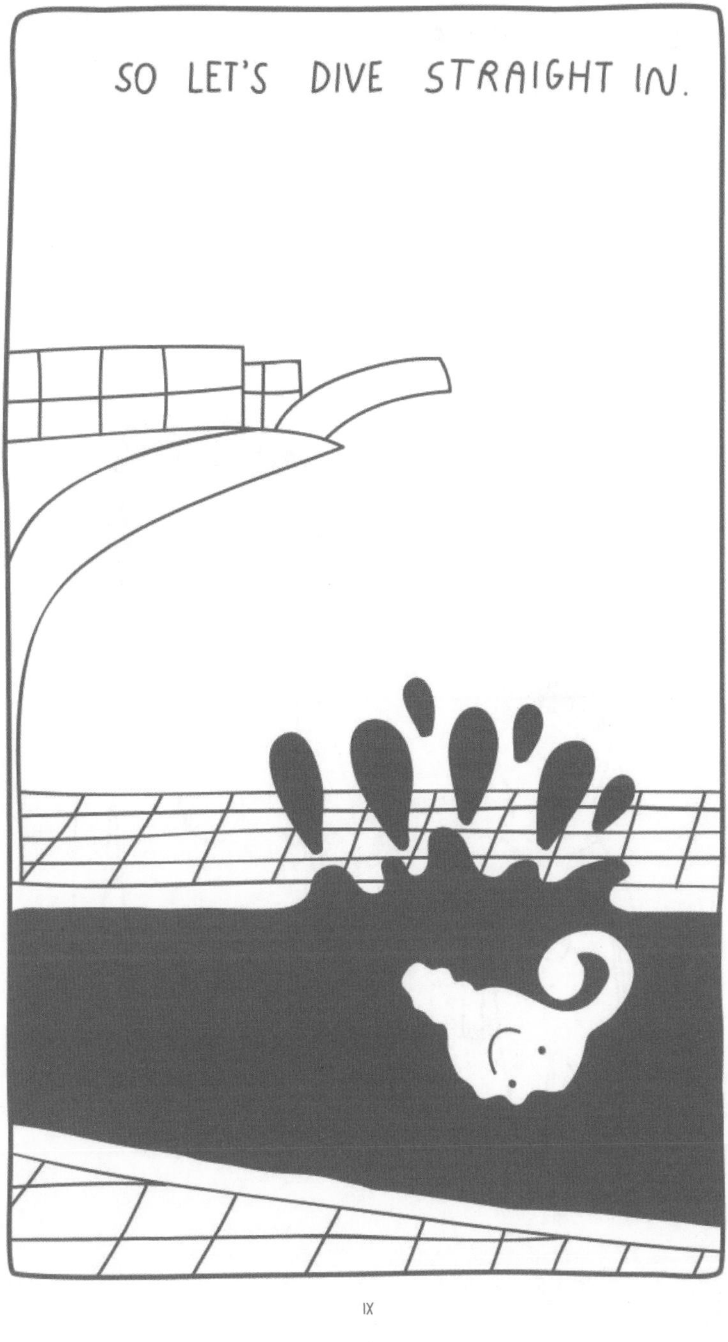
SO LET'S DIVE STRAIGHT IN.

AS WE GET OLDER,

OUR BODIES CHANGE.

ONE THING THAT CHANGES AS A FEMALE-BORN BODY GROWS UP, IS THE START OF MENSTRUATION, ALSO KNOWN AS A PERIOD.

PUT SIMPLY,
A PERIOD IS WHEN SOME BLOOD
FROM THE WOMB LEAVES THE BODY
THROUGH THE VAGINA.

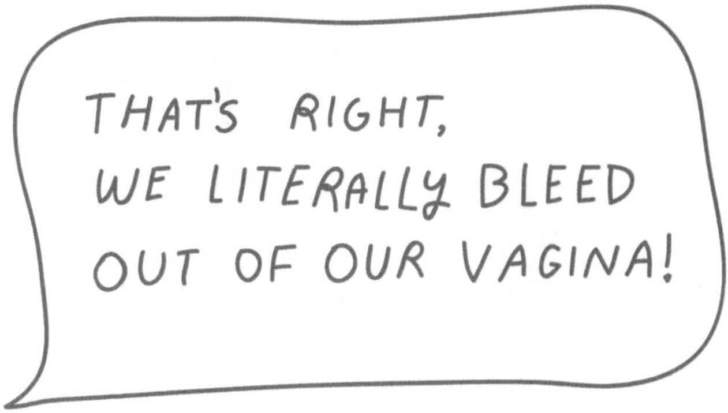
THAT'S RIGHT,
WE LITERALLY BLEED
OUT OF OUR VAGINA!

WE ALL DO!

ANYONE BORN WITH FEMALE PRIVATE
PARTS HAS A MENSTRUAL PERIOD. HAVING
A PERIOD OR NOT, DOESN'T DETERMINE
WHETHER YOU'RE A BOY OR GIRL, MAN
OR WOMAN.

WOMEN WHO ARE NOT BORN WITH
FEMALE PRIVATE PARTS MAY EXPERIENCE
ALL THE SYMPTOMS OF A PERIOD, JUST
WITHOUT THE   BLOOD.

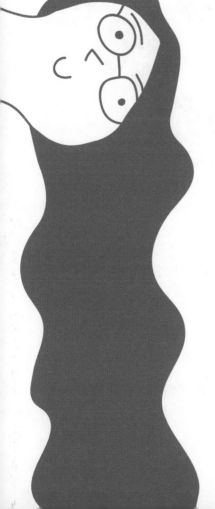

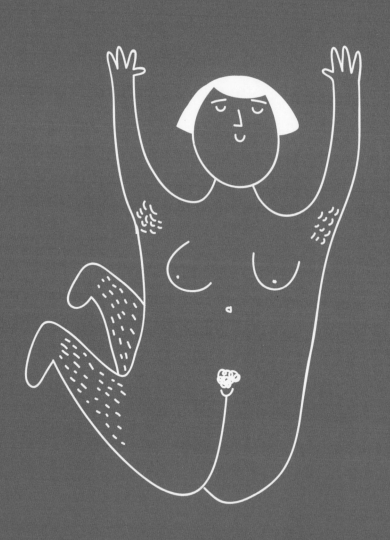

OUR BODIES

WHAT WE SEE

Our bodies are amazing and what we see is like an iceberg; we only see a bit and all the rest is inside.

ON THE OUTSIDE

MEET YOUR VULVA

A lot of people call what's between our legs the vagina, but that's not actually correct. The vagina refers to a specific part inside the body (see label). The outside of a female's private parts, or genitals, is called the vulva.

Genitals come in all shapes, sizes and colours. There is no perfect vulva. The medical word for this is "NORMAL VARIATION".

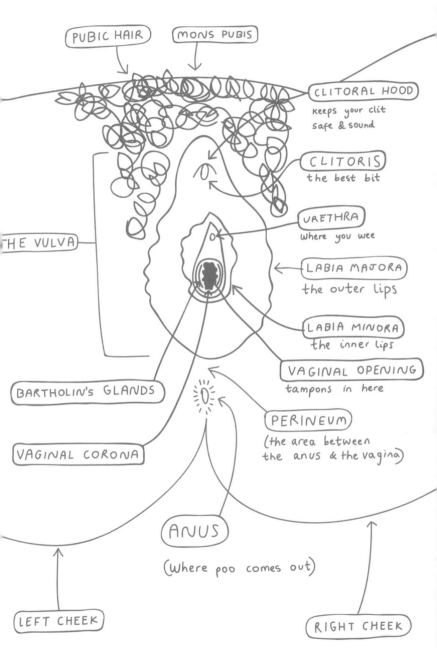

PUBIC HAIR

MONS PUBIS

CLITORAL HOOD
keeps your clit
safe & sound

CLITORIS
the best bit

URETHRA
where you wee

THE VULVA

LABIA MAJORA
the outer lips

LABIA MINORA
the inner lips

VAGINAL OPENING
tampons in here

BARTHOLIN'S GLANDS

VAGINAL CORONA

PERINEUM
(the area between
the anus & the vagina)

ANUS

(where poo comes out)

LEFT CHEEK

RIGHT CHEEK

7

HAVE A LOOK

Not only is it important to check if everything is A-okay, it's also empowering and a good way to build self-confidence and body positivity.

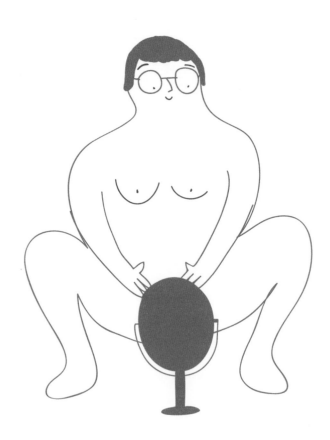

If you can get some privacy and a bit of time, grab a mirror, relax and try squatting in front of it with your legs open. Have a good look and get to know your body.

PUBIC HAIR

Pubic hair is going to be the first thing you see when looking at your private parts. Just like the hair on your head, your pubic hair is unique to you. A few fine hairs may begin to grow in childhood but pubic hair begins during puberty. It is one of the signs that your first period may well be on its way, as pubic hair develops due to the change in hormone levels.

Hormones are substances that typically occur naturally in your body to make an organ do something. Sex hormones are responsible for sexual development in puberty and then responsible for reproduction.

Pubic hair is found around the private parts and sometimes at the tops of the thighs. It is generally heavier, longer, curlier, rougher and coarser.

DID YOU KNOW?

You can do whatever you want to your pubic hair, it's your choice, so do whatever makes you feel most comfortable. Pubic hair is <u>not</u> something to feel ashamed of and no one should make you feel that way.

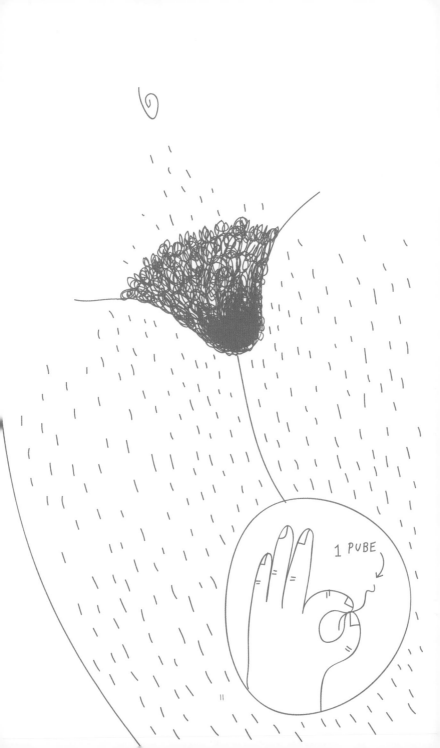

1 PUBE

MONS PUBIS

This is a rounded mass of fatty tissue over the pubic bone. Due to hormones this tends to be larger on the female body and after puberty will be covered in pubic hair. Another term for this is 'mons Veneris', which means the mountain of Venus. The purpose is to give cushioning and protection to the pubic bones and tissues lying underneath. The mons pubis is above the labia majora.

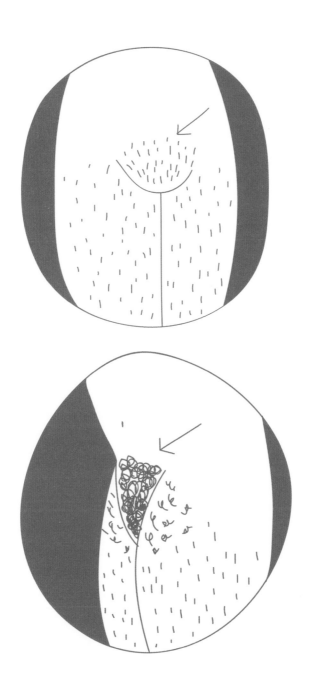

LET'S TALK

ABOUT LABIA

While holding your mirror, you will see a pair of folds of skin, this is the labia majora which literally means "great lips" in Latin. Their function is to cover and protect the vulva's most sensitive parts.

DID YOU KNOW?

It's actually really common to have one side of your labia majora bigger than the other. Most people don't have a completely symmetrical labia. Just like how most people have one foot bigger than the other, our labia are the same.

There's also nothing unusual about having a labia minora (little lip) that is bigger than the labia majora. Think of it like your belly button, there are outies and innies and they are all beautiful, amazing and most importantly, healthy. There are all kinds of different labia, but here are a few.

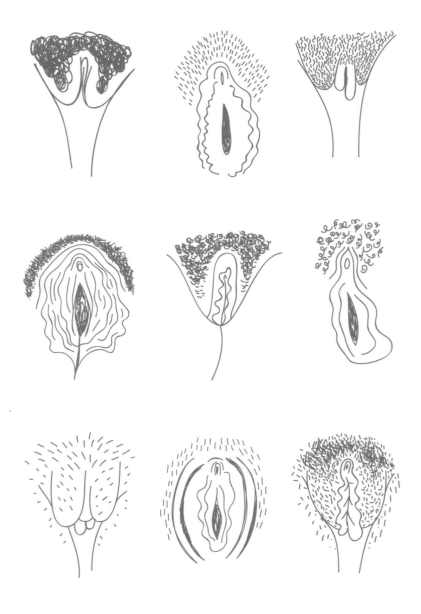

COLOUR

Just like the natural colour of your lips, the colour of our labia is unique to our body. From pink to red, purple or brown, dark, light or even the same colour as the rest of the skin.

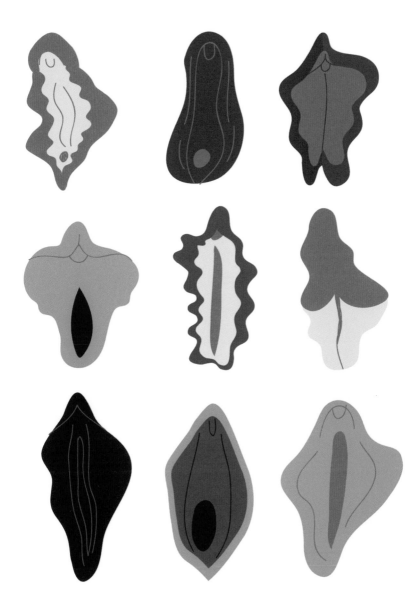

WILL MY LABIA CHANGE?

Your labia may change during puberty, pregnancy, with age or if your weight changes a lot. Each person's private parts are different and unique.

CLITORIS

Also called the clit, the bean, button or the jewel. Look between the inner lips right below your mons pubis and you will see the clitoral hood. Inside the hood is a bump about the size of a pea and this is the clitoris. Although you can only see a little bit, the clitoris goes far within your body. Remember the iceberg we talked about earlier - we only see the tip of the clitoris and the rest is inside our bodies. The whole clitoris inside and out is about the same size as a non-erect penis. It is usually the most sensitive spot of the vulva, as it has 15,000 nerve endings, twice as many as the penis. The clitoris is the only organ in the entire body with the sole purpose of giving pleasure.

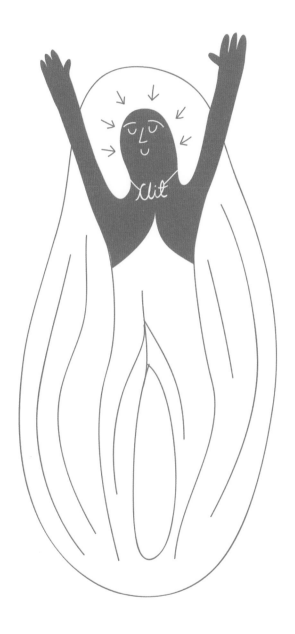

URETHRA

Looking lower than the clitoris you may be able to see another hood-like shape. Below that shape is a teeny-tiny hole, and that my friend is the urethra. This is the hole where you urinate, wee, tinkle, whiz, do a number one or drain the main vein. Whatever you like to call it, wee comes out of this hole above your vaginal opening.

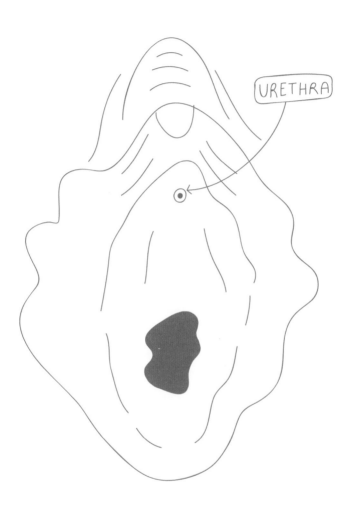

URETHRA

VAGINAL CORONA

Inside the opening of the vagina, about 1-2 centimetres in, there is the vaginal corona. It is thin folds of tissue and is stretchy. Every corona looks different.

DID YOU KNOW?

The corona has also been called the hymen. There are many dangerous beliefs about the hymen, but this is in fact a permanent part of the body, it doesn't disappear. It can't be broken when losing your virginity. The only time that the corona will change is during a vaginal birth.

Unfortunately we still don't know the function of the corona.

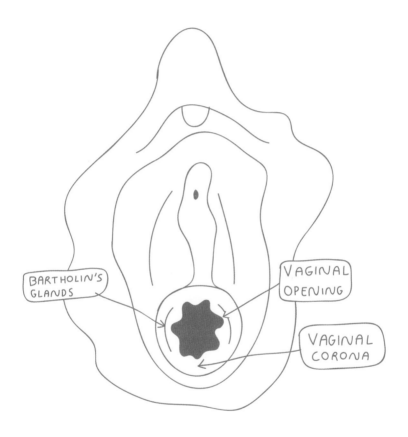

BARTHOLIN'S GLANDS

VAGINAL OPENING

VAGINAL CORONA

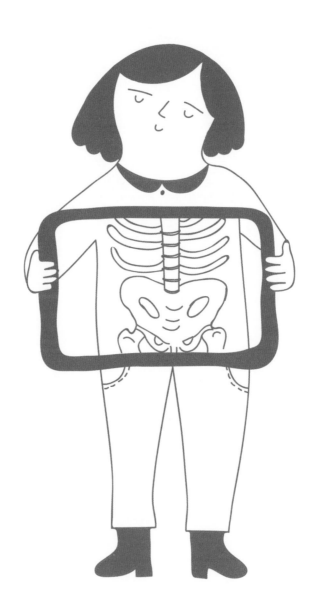

ON THE INSIDE

WHAT YOU CAN'T SEE

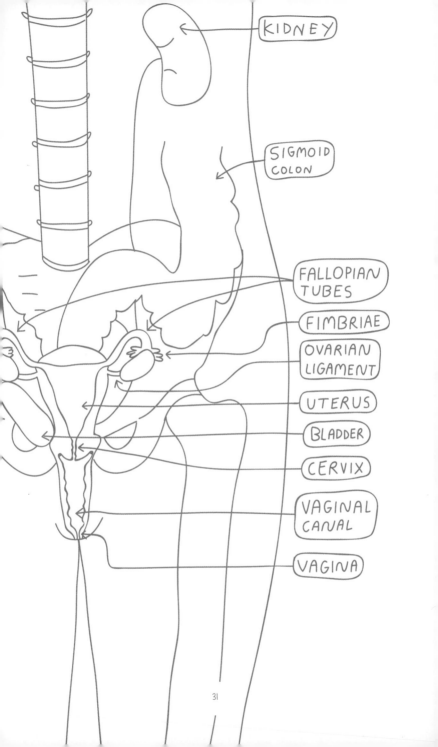

KIDNEY

SIGMOID COLON

FALLOPIAN TUBES

FIMBRIAE

OVARIAN LIGAMENT

UTERUS

BLADDER

CERVIX

VAGINAL CANAL

VAGINA

OVARIES

The ovaries are small, about the size of a walnut, located about one inch away from the uterus and are where the eggs are grown and released. They also make the hormones <u>oestrogen</u> and <u>progesterone</u> which are really important to our health (see page 62). They are pinkish-gray in color and have an uneven surface.

The most mature egg is released and swept through the fallopian tubes. The ovaries don't take it in turns from one side to another, it actually all happens quite randomly.

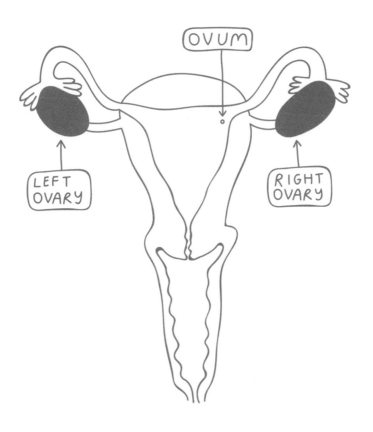

OVUM

Meet the ovum, also known as the egg. It's about the size of a grain of sand. The egg is matured in the ovary and enters the fallopian tube towards the uterus. Once in the tube it has 12-24 hours to live. If the egg doesn't come into contact with the sperm, it will just dissolve and pass out of the body along with the period blood.

If it does meet the sperm, several things happen all at once:
<u>Builds an electric fence</u> - the electric charge of the egg wall changes so no other sperm cells can enter. Only room for one I'm afraid, no room at the inn.
<u>Becomes hard & strong</u> - calcium is released, which causes the outer layer of the egg to change and harden, making it impenetrable.
<u>Zinc sparks</u> - strong bursts of zinc are released. There is now less zinc in the egg, which helps the cell's growth start again.

DID YOU KNOW?
- An egg is about 4 times bigger than a skin cell
- 16 times bigger than a sperm
- 26 times bigger than a red blood cell
- At the beginning of a cycle there are about 12 eggs that have begun to grow but only one of those gets to mature and be released

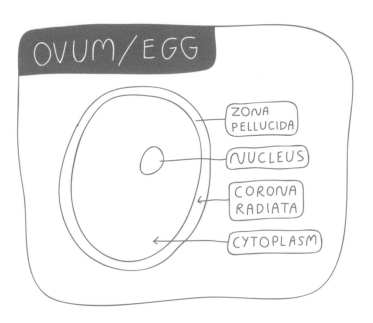

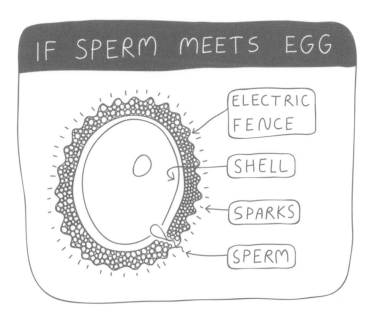

UTERUS

This is what your uterus looks like, its muscular walls form a pear shape. The job of the uterus is to look after the embryo by growing a thicker lining. This lining is shed to form period blood if the egg is not fertilsed. If the uterus owner wants to have a baby, the uterus will look after it. The uterus is amazing as it can expand when it needs to carry a baby and is <u>incredibly</u> strong.

Another word for this part of the body is the womb.

:

The uterus has 3 layers

ENDOMETRIUM - this layer surrounds the inside of the uterus and gets thinner and thicker at different times in your cycle.

MYOMETRIUM - the middle layer is muscle tissue, which is how the uterus can expand and then contract.

PERIMETRIUM - the outermost layer forms the external casing of the uterus, which adds extra strength.

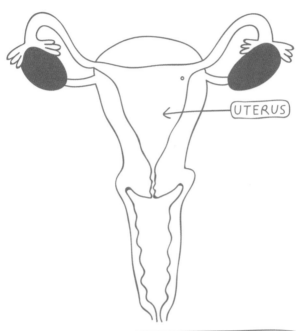

UTERUS

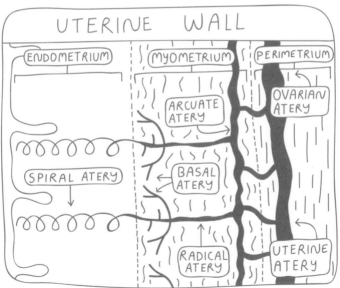

UTERINE WALL

ENDOMETRIUM MYOMETRIUM PERIMETRIUM

ARCUATE ATERY

OVARIAN ATERY

SPIRAL ATERY

BASAL ATERY

RADICAL ATERY

UTERINE ATERY

FALLOPIAN TUBES

Also known as the oviducts or uterine tubes, these are two thin tubes about 10cm long that connect the ovaries to the uterus. When the eggs get released they will be transported through the fallopian tubes to the uterus. These play a big role.

OVARIAN LIGAMENT
This connects the ovary to the uterus and helps hold the ovary in place.

FIMBRIAE
Are small fringer-like projections from the end of the fallopian tubes which hover near the ovaries and are activated by hormones. Their function is to help the egg, which has been released by the ovary, to move into the fallopian tube using a sweeping method.

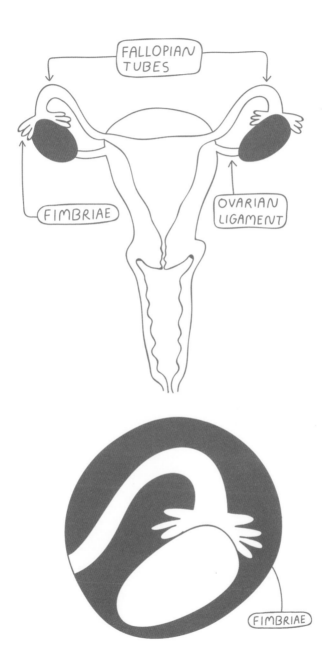

FALLOPIAN TUBES

FIMBRIAE

OVARIAN LIGAMENT

FIMBRIAE

CERVIX

The cervix, which in Latin means "the neck" of the uterus, is a cylinder-like shaped passage between the vaginal canal and the cavity of the uterus, which blood passes through when you have your period. At the end of the cervix, where it reaches the vagina, there is a small opening called the cervical os. When the cervix is closed, this looks like a dimple. The cervix directs the sperms into the uterus, protects the uterus from unwanted bacteria and viruses, makes its own lubrication and even grows a plug to seal the cervical canal during pregnancy.

The opening of the cervical canal is normally very narrow and usually about 2 - 3 cm long.

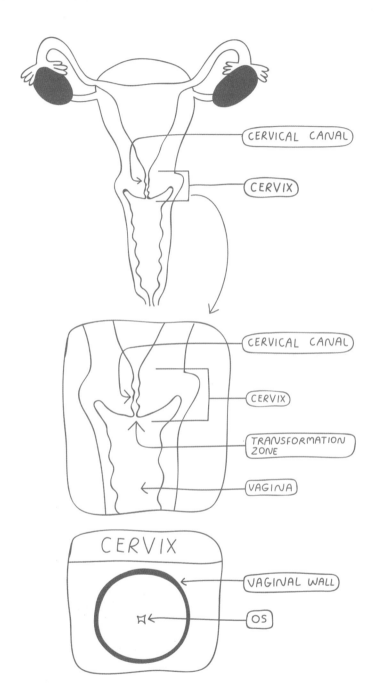

CERVICAL CANAL

CERVIX

CERVICAL CANAL

CERVIX

TRANSFORMATION ZONE

VAGINA

CERVIX

VAGINAL WALL

OS

HOW TO FIND YOUR CERVIX

Finding your own cervix can be tricky, so here are some steps to help you. Take your time and feel around, your cervix will be the only thing that will feel different to your walls. Its location and how squishy it feels will change depending on where you are in your cycle. It's most likely going to feel closer to your belly button than your back.

"I didn't really know what I was looking for. It took me a few days of being patient with myself, and getting used to my body, to finally find it."

SIDEWAYS

You can see here how close together the bladder, rectum and uterus are. Look, it's almost like a sandwich, the uterus is the filling between the two other organs. This means when you're menstruating, you may experience other symptoms, like needing to poo more (see page 164).

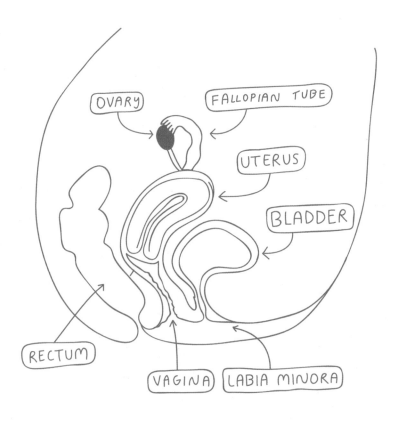

OVARY

FALLOPIAN TUBE

UTERUS

BLADDER

RECTUM

VAGINA

LABIA MINORA

* PLEASE NOTE
THE ABOVE DRAWING
IS <u>NOT</u> A SCIENTIFIC DRAWING,
IT IS FOR COMEDIC PURPOSES ONLY!

THE MENSTRUAL CYCLE

WHAT IS THE
MENSTRUAL
CYCLE?

The menstrual cycle is the time from the first day of your period to the day before your next period. It is called a cycle because it repeats itself from your very first period until menopause.

Now remember our beautiful bodies are unique so the menstrual cycle will vary from person to person. The average cycle is 28 days, but anything from 21 - 40 days is considered to be okay.

Within 1 cycle there are 4 different phases, some of which overlap. This chapter will talk about the phases according to the average 28-day cycle.

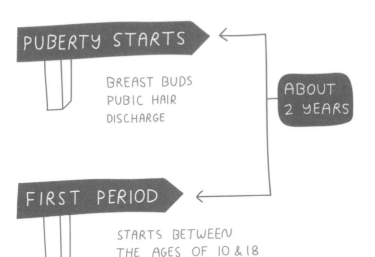

PUBERTY STARTS

BREAST BUDS
PUBIC HAIR
DISCHARGE

ABOUT
2 YEARS

FIRST PERIOD

STARTS BETWEEN
THE AGES OF 10 & 18

THE MENSTRUAL CYCLE STARTS

THE 1st YEAR – approx. 4 periods
THE 2nd YEAR – approx. 6 periods
3 – 5 YEARS – approx. 8 periods
ADULTS – approx. 9 periods in a year

MENOPAUSE BEGINS

TYPICALLY STARTS BETWEEN
45-55 YEARS OF AGE

THE FOUR PHASES

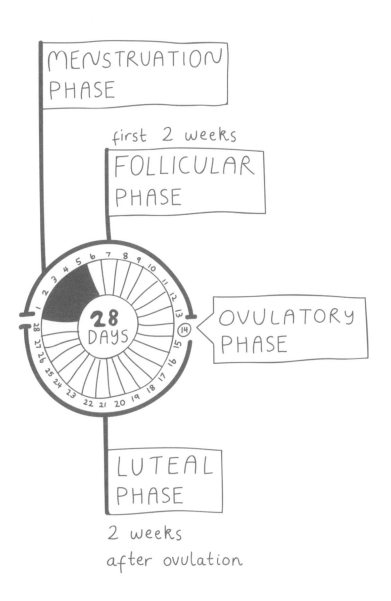

MENSTRUATION PHASE

first 2 weeks
FOLLICULAR PHASE

28 DAYS

OVULATORY PHASE

LUTEAL PHASE

2 weeks
after ovulation

MENSTRUATION PHASE

ROUGHLY
DAYS 1-5

The first day of your cycle is the first day of your period.

SCIENCE: the uterus lining (endometrium) is shed and released through the vagina along with some blood - although 5 days is typical, the menstruation phase can last up to 8 days

CERVIX: firm & low

CERVICAL FLUID: gel-like but you won't notice because of the blood

MAY FEEL: low, fatigued, tired, introverted and introspective

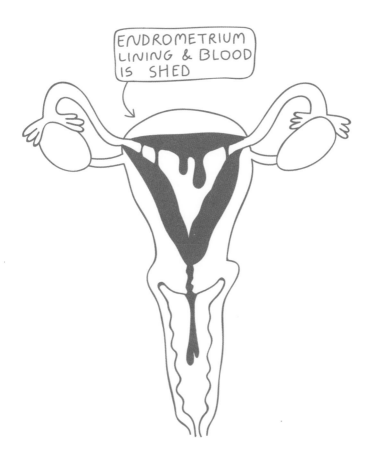

FOLLICULAR PHASE

ROUGHLY
DAYS 1-13

The first few days of the follicular phase overlap with the menstruation phase.

SCIENCE: your body is working on growing/developing those eggs and the lining of your womb thickens

CERVIX: firm and low to start with, then moves higher

CERVICAL FLUID: possibly dry at first (your vagina can feel drier) and then later wetter, looks creamy

MAY FEEL: your energy begin to increase, impulsive and lighter

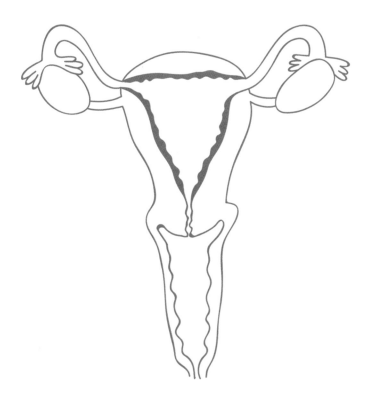

OVULATION PHASE

ROUGHLY
DAY 14

Ovulation is one day of the cycle.

SCIENCE: the ovary releases the dominant egg into the fallopian tube - the egg has 12-24 hours to be fertilised otherwise it just dies - the egg can be fertilised by sperm already in your womb, if you've recently had sex

CERVIX: soft and open

CERVICAL FLUID: clear, egg white, stretchy

MAY FEEL: confident & energetic

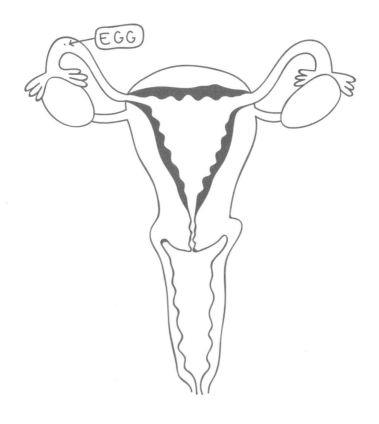

LUTEAL
PHASE

Now ovulation is done, we enter the luteal phase.

SCIENCE: the cells supporting the egg in ovulation change their duty and make progesterone, this causes the lining of the uterus to thicken ready to receive a fertilised egg - the last day of this phase is the day before your next period and the last day of your cycle

CERVIX: firm & closed

CERVICAL FLUID: sticky

MAY FEEL: a bit tired or down

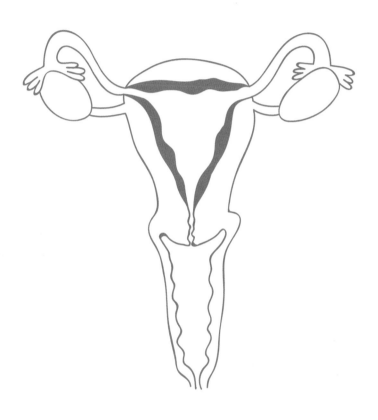

Nuts

Dark chocolate

Berries

Hummus

Bananas

MENSTRUATION

Listen to your body

Walking/jogging

Lavender

Chamomile

Connect

Carrots

Greens

Create

Broccoli

OVULATION

Pumpkin

Geranium

Clary sage

Kickboxing, HIIT

HORMONES

Hormones are chemical substances which act as messengers in the body. The main hormones in the menstrual cycle are oestrogen and progesterone, which have lots of different effects on the body.

Throughout the menstrual cycle hormones go up and down. These changes can make you feel more irritable before a period. Sometimes the symptoms are more severe and we call this premenstrual syndrome. You can read all about it in chapter 5.

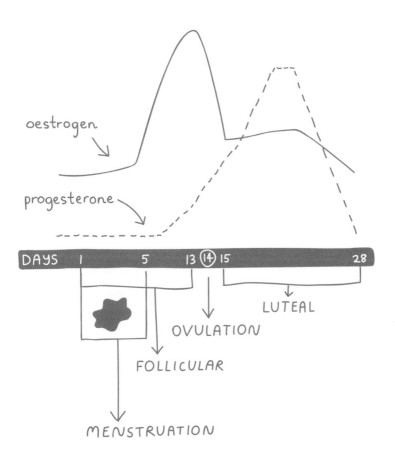

HORMONE LEVELS DURING
A 28-DAY CYCLE

oestrogen

progesterone

DAYS 1 5 13 (14) 15 28

MENSTRUATION

FOLLICULAR

OVULATION

LUTEAL

MENOPAUSE

Menopause is a part of the natural process of ageing and is when a womb-owner stops having periods. The average age for menopause is 51 but premature or early menopause can occur at any age. Sometimes menstruation can stop suddenly, or sometimes it can stop slowly over a number of years.

During this time hormones will change, which means most people will experience some symptoms. The most common are hot flushes, night sweats, difficulty sleeping, low mood, anxiety, reduced libido (desire to have sex) and problems with memory and focus.

This can be an extremely difficult time. If you know someone going through this try and reach out to them and offer support. If you are having a tough time with menopause there are ways to ease it and visiting a doctor can help.

TRACK
YOURS

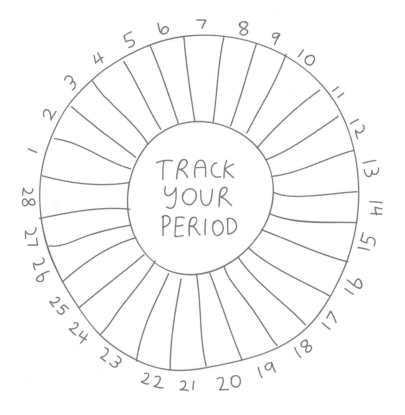

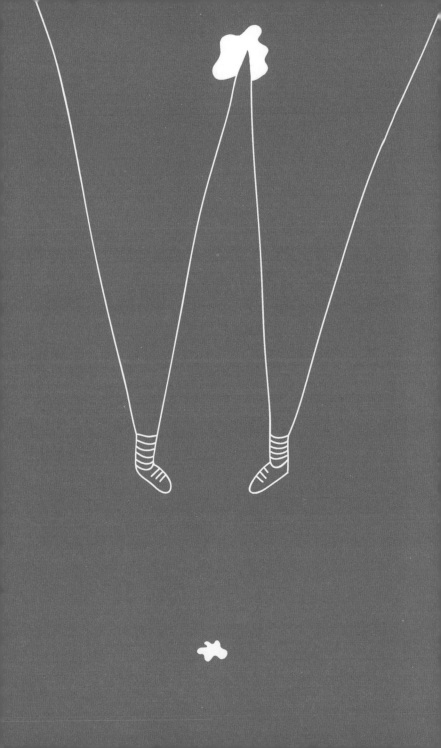

PERIOD
PRODUCTS

SO YOU'RE BLEEDING, NOW WHAT?

No need to worry, we've got you. This chapter will talk about all the different ways to care for your period. There are many different options out there. Try a couple out and see what makes you feel the most comfortable. What your friend does might not be the right fit for you. You know your body best and know what's right for you.

The easiest and most accessible way to find period care is to pop to your local supermarket. Go down the aisle with the toiletries and you will see products called pads, tampons, or panty liners, in all kinds of packaging.

Here's a heads up, they will most likely <u>not</u> use the word "period", "blood" or "menstruation" on them, so it's totally understandable if you get a little confused or overwhelmed. You might also feel a little bit embarrassed if it's new to you, but remember there's nothing to be ashamed of. More than half of the population have a period! <u>No one</u> is looking at you, <u>no one</u> is judging you.

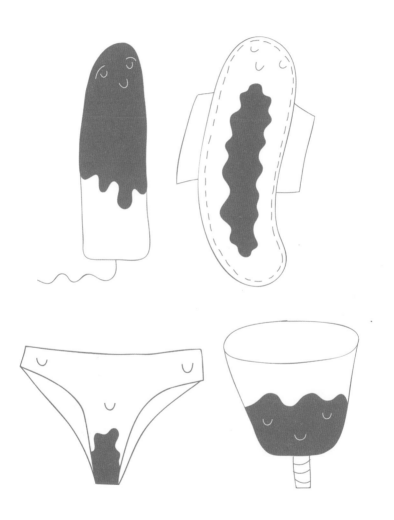

Over time you will understand all of the different products more so just take a deep breath, take your time and have a browse.

It's a good idea to try some methods out if you can. Walk around the house with them to get used to how they feel. You can even practice changing them when you're not on your period.

PADS

We are starting with pads because they are the easiest of all options, usually the first product anyone will use and recommended to beginners because they are the simplest.

Pads are the most popular method for period care.
A pad is a wad of absorbent material (either cotton or synthetic fibres) stuck onto the inside of your pants by a sticky adhesive strip, with or without wings that go around the side. The material absorbs the blood as it comes out of your vagina. There are loads of options to choose from so experiment to see what works best.

DIFFERENT OPTIONS

Choose according to your body and knickers

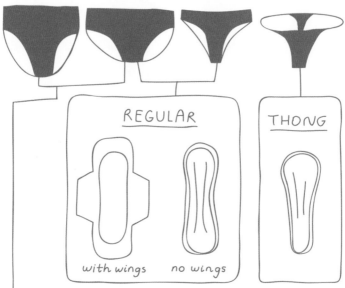

REGULAR

with wings

no wings

THONG

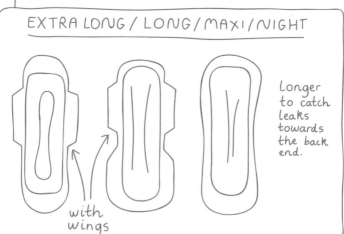

EXTRA LONG / LONG / MAXI / NIGHT

with wings

Longer to catch leaks towards the back end.

OTHER

 Panty liners are for light days, spotting or discharge

MATERIALS

* Synthetic materials
* Cotton
* Silk cotton
* Organic cotton
* Bamboo

YOUR FLOW	Very Light	Light	Medium	Heavy
PAD THICKNESS	Ultra thin	Thin	Regular	Maxi/ Super

Singular packaging

CHANGE EVERY 3-4 HOURS

HOW TO:

USE IT

❤ 1   Peel off the wrapping

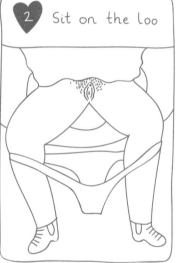

❤ 2   Sit on the loo

❤ 3   Stick it on

← fold
the
wings

CHANGE IT

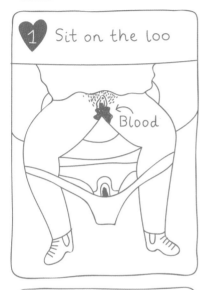

1 Sit on the loo

Blood

2 Peel off

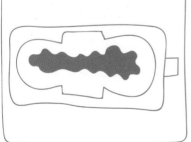

3 Stick a new one on & put the used one in the new wrapper or toilet roll

4 Roll it

5 Bin it

Remember someone has to empty that bin, so leave it as you would like to find it

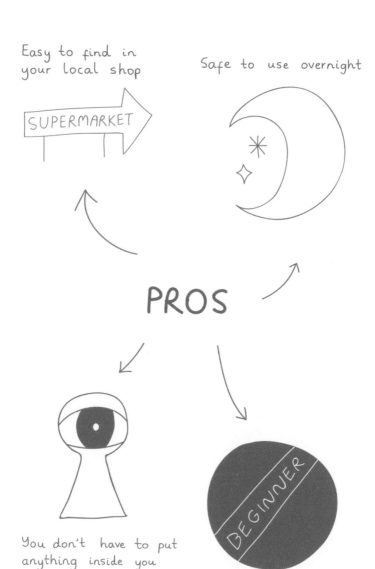

Easy to find in your local shop

Safe to use overnight

SUPERMARKET

PROS

You don't have to put anything inside you

Easy to use, especially for beginners

BEGINNER

Less freedom for activities -
you can't swim with one

Standard pads are not
enviromentally friendly

CONS

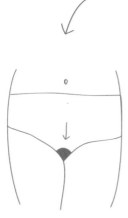

You can feel it
in your pants

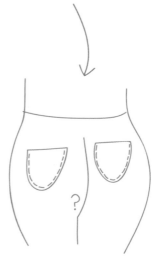

You may be able to see
bigger pads in tight clothing

CLOTH PADS

If you like pads but are looking for an enviromentally friendly option, cloth pads might be what you're after. There are a lot of options to choose from with different fabrics or designs, which are really pretty. They work like regular pads, but after using them you just wash them and reuse them (when dry).

"It can take a while to get used to the feeling of wearing a pad. When I was at school I was so paranoid that you could see it through my trousers I used to make my BFF walk behind me and check if it was visible, but it was always fine. I prefer using pads because I have a heavy flow so it's the most comfortable for me. I've leaked less with pads and I just feel a bit safer, like everything is going to be fine. I also always lose track of time, but with pads I know when I need to change it. I love my pads and I am a proud pad-wearer!"

WE L♡VE

FLO PADS

They are made out of bamboo
so are super eco-friendly
and kind to your body.

hereweflo.co

TAMPONS

The next most popular option is tampons.
A tampon is made from cotton or synthetic
material which absorbs the period blood.
Essentially it works like a plug; you insert
it inside your vagina where it sits with a piece
of string hanging out. You then take it out using
this string and throw it away. You can get
tampons in lots of different options too,
depending on your flow.

DIFFERENT OPTIONS

YOUR FLOW	SIZES
Very Light	Slim
Light	Regular
Medium	Super
	Super Plus
Heavy	Ultra

CHANGE EVERY 4 HOURS

Applicator - free

Applicator

Singular packaging

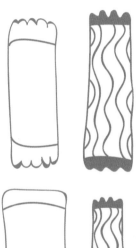

HOW TO:

USE IT

1. First locate your vaginal opening

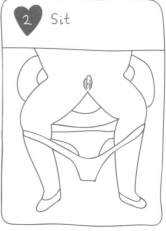

2. Sit

3. Relax

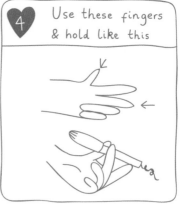

4. Use these fingers & hold like this

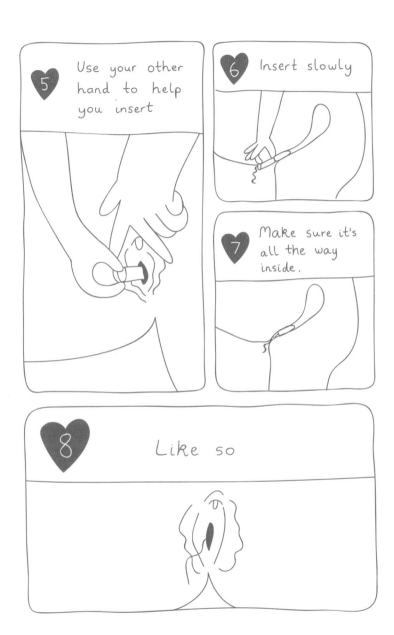

5 Use your other hand to help you insert

6 Insert slowly

7 Make sure it's all the way inside.

8 Like so

93

CHANGE IT

1 Sit

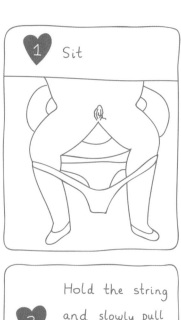

2 Relax

3 Hold the string and slowly pull it down until it's out

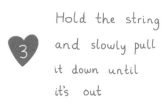

4 Roll it in loo roll

5 BIN IT

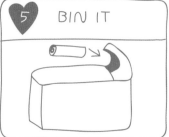

WHAT IF THERE ISN'T A BIN?

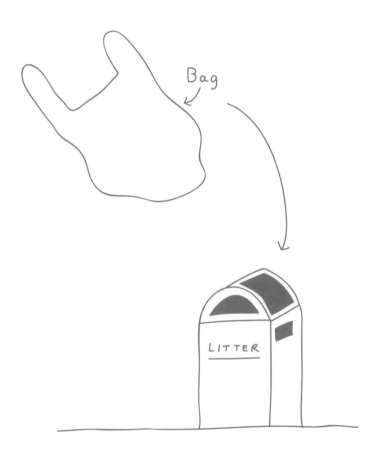

Bag

LITTER

You can move freely and
swim with a tampon in

You can't feel
anything wet

PROS

Can pop it in
your pocket

Internal so more discreet

Not always environmentally friendly

You can forget about them really easily

Fibres can be left inside your body

Can cause dryness

CONS

Can increase cramps for some people

Insertion needed

At risk of toxic shock syndrome

TSS

a rare but life-threatening condition caused by bacteria getting into the body and releasing harmful toxins

"I started using pads first and then tried tampons out when I wanted to go swimming on my period. It was really scary at first and it took me a long time in the bathroom to figure it all out, but I got there in the end. Now I find changing them a breeze. I started out with the applicator ones but now I just use the non-applicator ones, they are the most comfortable method for my body. On my heaviest day I might use a panty liner too. I am a proud tampon-wearer and I feel no shame in holding one on my way to the bathroom."

WE L♥VE

OHNE

100% organic tampons
delivered to your door
in all different sizes.

Ohne.co

MENSTRUAL CUPS

Menstrual cups are small flexible silicone or latex cups that you put up your vagina. You fold it and put it up and it opens inside the vaginal canal below the cervix, usually with a small pop which you might feel. When the cup opens it creates a vacuum and stays put collecting the blood. You then empty it out into the loo, rinse or wipe and pop it back in.

DIFFERENT OPTIONS

Instead of a absorbing blood
cups collect about 20-30ml

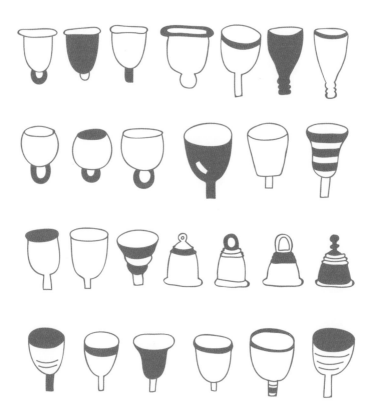

MATERIALS

* Medical-grade silicone
* Thermoplastic elastomer (TPE)

THEY VARY IN:

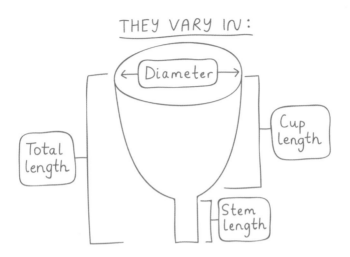

Diameter

Cup length

Total length

Stem length

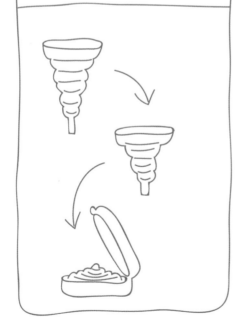

You can now get cups that fold away

Depending on your flow you might empty it out more regularly.

CHANGE EVERY 12 HOURS

HOW TO:

USE IT

 1 Sterilise the cup in boiling water for 3-4 minutes

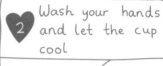 2 Wash your hands and let the cup cool

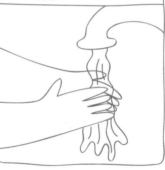

 3 Find a comfortable position

Squat, put one foot up, or sit on the toilet

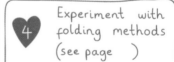 4 Experiment with folding methods (see page)

5 Completely relax

 **6** Insert the folded cup in your vagina

(You may want to use lubricant or water to make this easier. If you're using lubricant, place a little on the rim.)

7 Push in as far as comfortable then remove your fingers and let the cup pop open

8 If you feel any dents or folds, gently hold the base of the cup with your finger and rotate until it pops

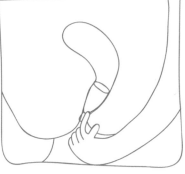

9 If you feel resistance from the stem, a vacuum has been created

EMPTY

Most people empty the cup 2-4 times a day depending on their flow

Use warm water or a mild perfume-free soap to wash your hands

 Relax

3 Get in a position comfortable for you

4

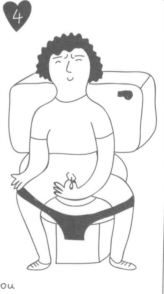

Pull on the stem while pushing with your vagina and stomach (like when you go to the toilet)

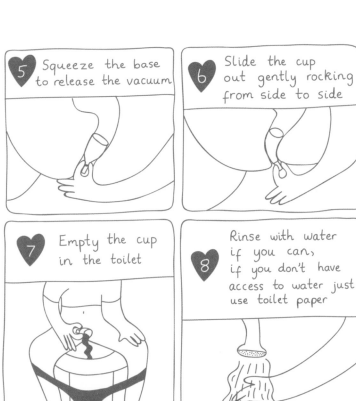

5 Squeeze the base to release the vacuum

6 Slide the cup out gently rocking from side to side

7 Empty the cup in the toilet

8 Rinse with water if you can, if you don't have access to water just use toilet paper

9 If your period has ended, boil again and store

Otherwise pop it back in

FOLDS

There are lots of different ways to fold
a menstrual cup and some will work for
you and others won't. Instructions should come with
your menstrual cup and if not, you can
research them online. Here are a couple of
the most popular:

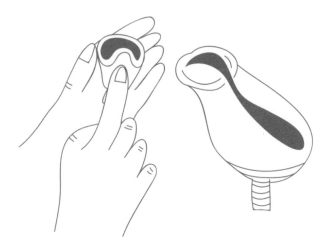

PUNCH-DOWN FOLD

Using one hand, take your index finger and
push the front rim down all the way into
the cup. Use the other hand to squeeze the top
so you can release your index finger. Use your
free hand to squeeze the base and let go
with the other hand. Insert the pointy tip into
your vagina.

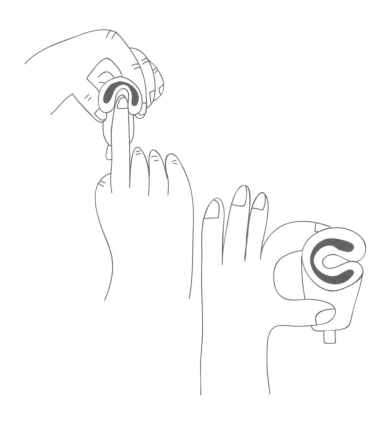

C-FOLD

Using two hands flatten the cup and then fold it in half. You will see a c-shape. You can also use your index finger to push one side of the cup until it is touching the other. Hold the whole thing tightly and insert.

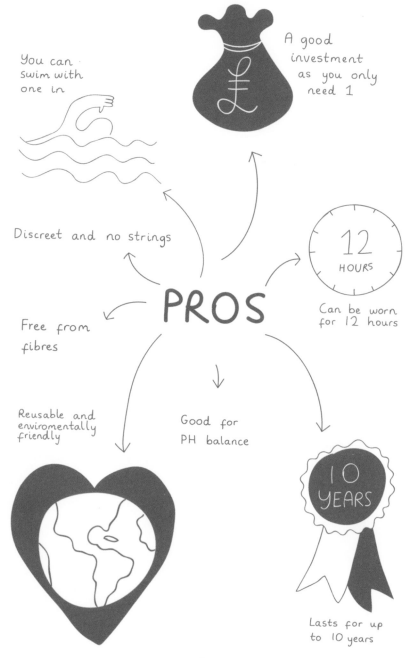

You can swim with one in

A good investment as you only need 1

Discreet and no strings

12 HOURS

Can be worn for 12 hours

Free from fibres

PROS

Reusable and enviromentally friendly

Good for PH balance

10 YEARS

Lasts for up to 10 years

Takes some time getting used to and can be difficult to use for some people

More expensive initially

CONS

More messy

They need cleaning

You need somewhere private to change it

"I was really worried about trying the menstrual cup at first because I didn't get along with tampons. It was a bit tricky, but I relaxed and took my time. For the first year I only used it at home because it took me a while to figure out which method of folding was right for me. When I started to get confident and found a fold that worked for me, I began to leave the house with it and wore a pad. Now it's been 4 years and it's the only method I use. I still find it quite daunting changing it in a public toilet but overall I love it. It's cut my period length in half and I barely have cramps now, not to mention all the extra cash I have."

WE L♡VE

INTIMINA

They have loads of different shapes
and sizes and some that fold down
into a cute compact case.

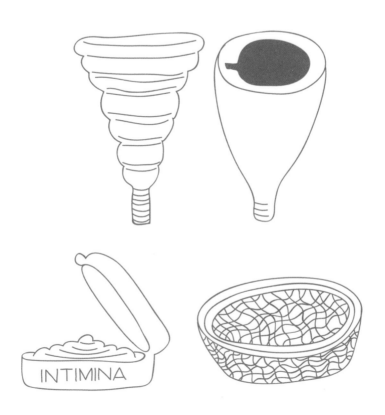

INTIMINA

intimina.com

PERIOD
UNDERWEAR

Still a relatively new product on the scene, period underwear is another really exciting modern choice. Using layers of different materials these pants actually hold and absorb your period blood. There are lots of different options out there for you to choose from. They are eco-friendly, look great and are comfy. You may feel the blood against you, like when you use a pad, but it doesn't feel wet.

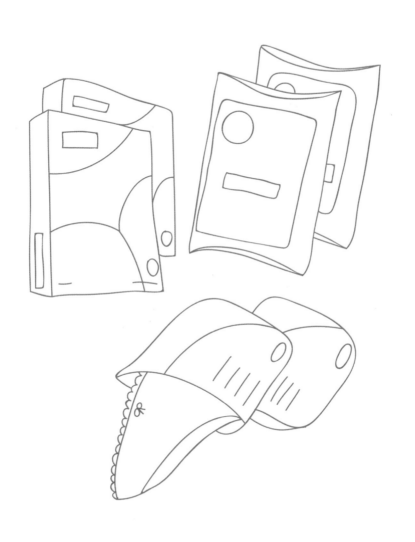

DIFFERENT OPTIONS

Lots of shapes and sizes just like normal pants

High waisted

Boy short

Thong

Bikini

Detachable

MATERIALS

Usually a mix of cotton, nylon and other synthetic materials for the outside, and 4 different layers for the absorbent inside.

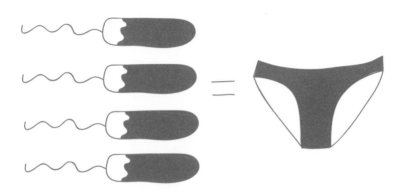

CHANGE EVERY
12
HOURS

HOW TO:

USE IT

1 Grab your pants

2 Put them on

CLEAN

1 Rinse with cold water

2 Wash without bleach or fabric softener

3 You <u>mustn't</u> put them in the tumble dryer so hang them up to dry

If you can put on pants
you can use these

Not wet

PROS

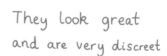

They look great
and are very discreet

Reusable and
enviromentally
friendly

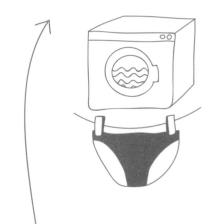
You've got to wash them and wait for them to dry

Can be expensive

CONS

Can get a little sweaty

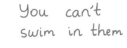
You can't swim in them

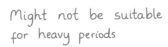
Might not be suitable for heavy periods

WE L♥VE

FLUX

They have a great detachable period pant, so if you want to change them without taking off the rest of your clothes, you can!

fluxundies.com

"I love using period underwear. I wear underwear everyday, so it's no extra hassle. On my heavier days I will sometimes wear a cup or tampon with them and that has been working well for me. I used to stain the bed all the time, but that doesn't happen now. I feel comfortable, secure and the freedom of not worrying about leaks feels great."

PERIOD POVERTY

Not everyone has the luxury of being able to choose what they use. Period products are far too expensive and it's absolutely ridiculous that they are not free for those in need. People living in poverty often have to make their own period protection with toilet paper, clothing or newspaper. Some have to go without anything at all.

WHO SUFFERS

- School children
- Refugees
- Asylum seekers
- Homeless people
- People in prison

IF YOU NEED HELP

Visit the Bloody Good Period (BGP) website for drop-in centres where you can pick up pads.

WAYS YOU CAN HELP

- Join the #FREEPERIODS movement
- Write to your MP about the issue
- Donate period products or your time to local and national organisations such as BGP and The Red Box project
- Donate to food banks through The Trussell Trust
- Look out for collections at your local supermarket

TO MY MP

BUSTING PERIOD PRODUCT MYTHS

* You <u>can</u> still pee and poop when using all menstrual products and you don't need to change them every time you go.

* You <u>can</u> use tampons or menstrual products if you have never had sex - it's perfectly safe, nothing is going to break or harm you.

* You <u>can</u> use tampons or cups for your first period, although it might be a little bit scary and overwhelming.

* You <u>can</u> take a bath or swim with your tampon or cup in.

* You <u>can</u> use old tampons as long as the packaging isn't ripped.

* You <u>cannot</u> get endometriosis (a condition where the tissue that lines the womb is found outside the womb) from wearing tampons.

* You <u>can</u> use a cup/tampon if you have endometriosis, just check with your doctor first.

* Tampons <u>cannot</u> get lost inside you. They may get stuck if you lose the string but with some feeling around you should be able to get it. If you don't feel comfortable doing this or you can't find it you should go to the doctors.

TOP TIP

Do not touch   private parts
after handling spicy food!

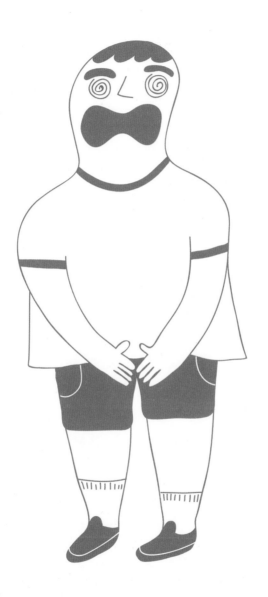

HEALTHY
DOWN THERE

IS EVERYTHING OKAY?

Although our bodies are strong, they are complicated and so things can go wrong. Infections down there are really common. They do not mean you are dirty, they do not mean there is something wrong with you. Vaginas are sensitive souls and can be thrown off balance easily.

In this chapter we look at the kind of things that can happen.

PERIOD BLOOD

Let's get one thing straight, period blood is not dirty or gross or smelly! It's just blood that happens to come out of the vagina.

Most of us lose between 6 and 16 teaspoons of blood during our periods (mostly in the first few days). Not to worry though, your body makes up for it.

SO WHAT DOES THE COLOUR OF YOUR BLOOD MEAN?

The changes in your period blood colour depend on how long you've been bleeding for or how long it has been exposed to air. The lining does not separate all in one go, it's a slow process of release.

Bright red = new fresh blood

Dark red = old blood

Brown / black = old blood

Pink = spotting

CLOTTING

Clots can be a little bit scary when you first
see them just because they are unlike anything you
will have seen before. They are a thick, lumpy
substance made of blood and tissue. They kinda
look like blackberry or raspberry jam (without the seeds).
It's totally healthy to pass period clots each
month so don't panic. If you are seeing very big clots
and they are frequent then you should consult
a doctor.

SPOTTING

Spotting is light bleeding that happens between periods. This may be annoying but is very common. It is useful to keep track of your bleeding, and if you are spotting regularly you should check in with your doctor.

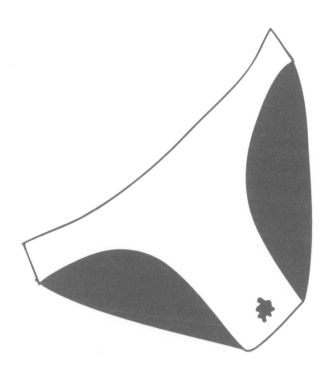

IRREGULAR PERIODS

It's okay to miss a period occasionally.
Try not to hide your head in the sand though,
there are lots of reasons to miss a period and it's
important to know what's going on so you tackle
any issues.

COMMON CAUSES OF AN IRREGULAR CYCLE:

* Puberty—periods can be irregular for the first couple of years
* Pregnancy
* Rapid weight gain
* Extreme weight loss
* Eating disorders
* Excessive exercise
* Contraception / birth control
* Medication
* Mental health issues
* Times of high stress / emotion / anxiety
* The start of menopause - when periods end
* Polycystic ovary syndrome - a common condition
that affects how ovaries function
* Ovarian cysts - a fluid-filled sac that develops on an
ovary, they are very common and often have no symptoms.

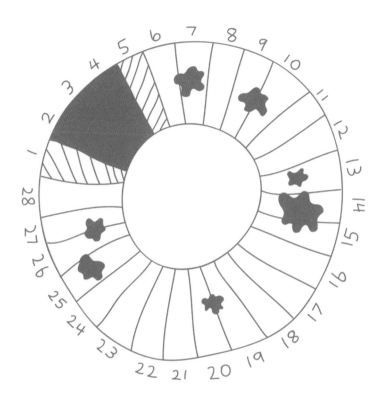

OTHER CAUSES:
* Overactive thyroid - when the thyroid
(found in your neck) produces too many hormones
* STIs - sexually transmitted infections, picked up
during unsafe sex, such as chlamydia and gonorrhoea

HEAVY PERIODS

Extremely heavy periods can be really tough to deal with. Sometimes there's no reason for bleeding so much and other times they can be a sign of something happening down there.

SOME CAUSES OF BLEEDING VERY HEAVILY

* Uterine fibroids - when growths develop in and around the uterus
* Endometriosis - a condition where the tissue that lines the womb is found in other parts of your body, such as the fallopian tubes
* Pelvic inflammatory disease (PID) - an infection of the organs of the reproductive system (the uterus, ovaries, fallopian tubes)
* Cancer - there are different gynaecological cancers; uterine, ovarian, cervical, vaginal and vulval

DOCTORS VISIT

YOU SHOULD SEE A DOCTOR IF:
* You don't have a period for 3 months
* Periods become irregular suddenly
* You bleed for more than 7 days
* You have to change your tampon every 1-2 hours
* Severe pain
* Spotting between periods regulary

QUESTIONS YOUR DOCTOR MAY ASK:
* Whether you are experiencing any stress or emotional issues
* Any changes in your weight
* Your sexual history
* How much you exercise

THE MEDICAL TESTS THEY MAY DO INCLUDE:

* A pelvic examination – this will involve a doctor looking at your reproductive organs internally and externally – you are welcome to ask for a chaperone to be present, if you feel a little worried or uncomfortable
* Blood tests
* Different types of ultrasound – a scan that uses sound waves to create an image of part of the inside of the body
* MRI – a scan that uses magnetic fields and radio waves to create an image of part of the inside of the body

REMEMBER

A doctor might be a professional, but you know your own body. If you are in pain or worried make sure your voice is heard. Take someone as back-up if you don't think you are being listened to.

"I missed about four months of my period during university. Two years later I was diagnosed with GAD (generalised anxiety disorder). Looking back I wish I had paid closer attention to my periods as I maybe could have recognised my anxiety sooner and got the help I needed, instead of suffering in silence for so long."

DISCHARGE

The vagina is an incredible self-cleaning machine.
Your body is hard at work all the time without
you even knowing it. Discharge is a fluid that
cleans the vagina and keeps it happy. It comes out
of the vagina and so you might see it in your
pants. Some people will see it a lot and others hardly
at all. It's totally okay and nothing to get
embarrassed about.

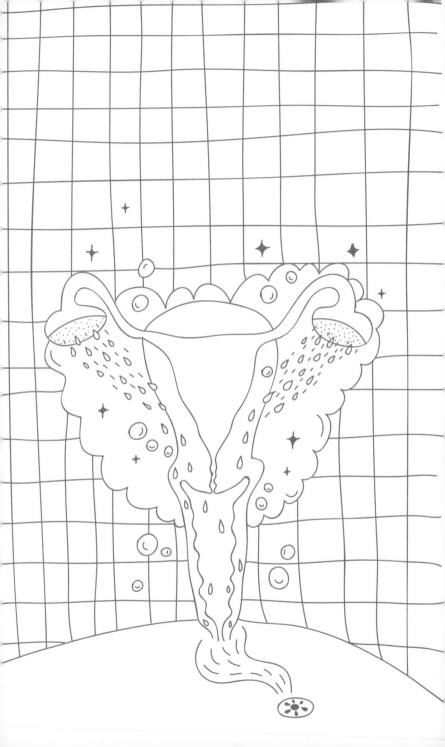

PHASES

If you pay attention to it, discharge can be a useful tool. Different textures and colours can show you where about in the menstrual cycle you are and whether your vagina is content.

Discharge can be clear, wet, thick, white or slippery. If you notice a change in colour or smell, particularly if you get a whiff of something fishy, it may indicate an infection of some sort.

DRY PHASE
not fertile

STICKY PHASE
not fertile

CREAMY PHASE
semi-fertile

CLEAR PHASE
fertility magic!

"I didn't know what it was and for years I thought something was wrong with me. I was embarrassed about it and felt so alone for a long time.
It knocked my self-esteem and confidence.
I often get so much it goes down my thighs.
I finally went to a gynaecologist and I was told I was totally normal and healthy. I feel comfortable now and I wear a panty liner most days. I've opened up to my friends and found I am not alone.
I'm learning to accept and love my body and I've never felt happier in my skin."

COMMON PROBLEMS

THRUSH

Thrush is a yeast infection caused by a fungus
that exists naturally in the body.
⊕ Symptoms: itchiness, soreness around the entry of the
vagina, stingy pee, swollen and inflamed
Ⓓ Discharge: white, thick, lumpy
⊖ Causes: skin irritation from tight clothes, pads and
synthetic materials, can be triggered by sex,
hormonal changes and taking antibiotics
⊕ Treatment: tablets or cream available from the pharmacy

BACTERIAL VAGINOSIS OR BV

BV is a change in the bacteria in the vagina.
⊕ Symptoms: a strong fishy smell, white or grey
watery discharge
⊖ Causes: using perfumed products in and around your
vagina, being sexually active, changing partner, the IUD
(a device put inside the uterus to stop pregnancy)
⊕ Treatment: antibiotics or gel from the doctor

UTI / CYSTITIS

A urinary tract infection is an infection of any part
of the urinary system (the bits in charge of peeing).
⊙ Symptoms: burning sensation when peeing, the need
to pee a lot but only a dribble coming out, tiredness,
feeling unwell, tummy pain and maybe blood in your wee
⊙ Causes: bacteria in the urethra
⊕ Treatment: drinking water, cranberry tablets, painkillers,
hot water bottle or antibiotics from the doctor

WAYS YOU CAN PREVENT THEM

Infections have been linked to tight clothing

Wash regularly
(avoiding perfumed soap)

Be careful taking antibiotics as it can result in an imbalance down there

Drinking plenty of water

Changing your pad / tampon enough times in a day

Pee and drink water after sex

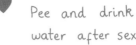

100% cotton underwear is your best friend

Wipe front to back

Sleeping without underwear

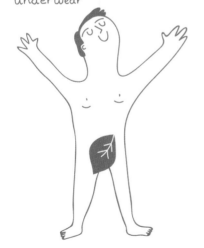

Eating probiotics such as :
Yoghurt
Sauerkraut
Tempeh
Kimchi
Miso
Kombucha
Pickles

SWEATY VULVA

It's important to know that just like your armpits, your crotch has a lot of sweat producing glands too. If it's warm or you are doing anything that makes you hot and bothered you will get a little sweaty down there.

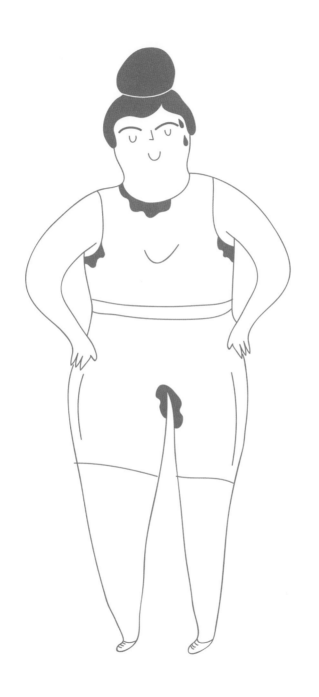

LET'S TALK POOP

You may notice that on the first days of your period you are going for number twos more regulary. This is because one of the hormone substances in your uterus (called prostaglandins) makes your muscles contract or tighten to push the lining out. Unfortunately, it can also impact the organs near by. As we saw from the sideways diagram earlier, where we number 2 is really close to the uterus, so as well as helping to push the lining out, it can make you need the toilet more. This may come in the form of diarrhoea (watery poo) or going to the loo more.

FEELING GOOD

OVERCOMING PMS

I am not a doctor or a scientist and I'm certainly not the smartest pea in the pod, but I have had periods for over 15 years so I have got some good experience under my belt (literally).
When I was younger I had heavy, excruciating periods and wouldn't be able to get out of bed. I physically couldn't go to school and so I fell behind. As I've grown up my periods have gotten lighter, more regular and more on the manageable side. What has really helped me to cope is having more information. Now I am able to reduce my cramps and I listen to my body to give it what it needs.

In this chapter I want to give you some tools to learn how to feel good on your period. An average womb-owner will bleed for a total number of days equivalent to ten years of their life. If our attitude towards menstruation is negative, that's going to have a negative impact on our lives. Bleeding may be uncomfortable and painful, but if we think about it positively and learn as much as possible, it'll help us to cope with those ten years a little bit better.

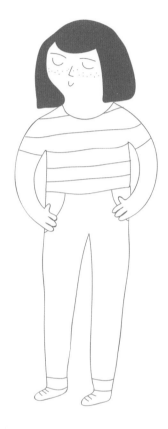

One thing that affects a bunch of people is PMS
or premenstrual syndrome. Although not quite
understood by doctors yet, it is thought that it
is caused by your hormones going up and down.
Whatever it is, it can get you down,
both physically and mentally.

COMMON SYMPTOMS OF PMS

Bloating

Change in appetite

Tender breasts

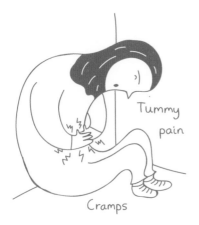

Tummy pain

Cramps

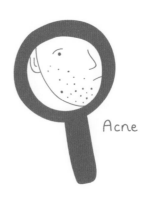

Acne

Mood swings

Feeling upset

Feeling angry

Feeling anxious

Feeling tired

HOW TO
TREAT PMS

Having a life without PMS completely taking over IS POSSIBLE; it's about looking at daily choices and questioning how they could be affecting and influencing the balance of your health and your hormones. Everyone has different PMS triggers so just experiment to find yours. You will begin to see just how much your body is affected by what you put in it.

Write down what symptoms you have, what you are eating, how much you are moving and how you're feeling. By keeping this journal you will begin to see the patterns.

Your body will always tell you how it feels, you just need to listen. If your PMS or emotions are getting in the way of you living your everyday life, please see a doctor. You don't have to suffer in silence.

CRAMPS

The fancy pants name of painful period cramps is dysmenorrhoea. The pain is caused by uterine muscle contractions (caused by our friend prostagladin on page 164) and the pain is felt in the lower tummy. For some the discomfort can be annoying, for others it can be dreadful and they can feel cramps all the way up their back and down their thighs. They can be so severe that they really interfere with life.

Conditions such as endometriosis and uterine fibroids can also cause severe menstrual cramps. If your cramps are affecting you, go to see a doctor as there are options available.

Cramps can happen 24-48 hours before your period and for a lot of people that's a sign that they need to get some period products soon. Others get cramps later on in their period or during their heaviest days. Here are some ways to relieve cramps.

Ginger

Bananas

Nuts & seeds

Lemon

Applying heat

Chamomile tea

Raspberry tea

Pineapple

Water

A warm bath

Spicy food

Dark chocolate

Exercise such as yoga movements

Orgasms

BLOATING

Lots of people with periods experience a puffy belly, stomach discomfort or a swollen abdomen. It happens because contractions of the uterus affect how quickly the food moves through the digestive system.

There are other factors that make you bloat, such as water retention (a build up of fluids inside the body). It's very common for people who bloat to gain up to 10 pounds during their period. But like a lot of PMS there's ways to ease it. Here are a few.

Eat slower

Rub your tummy clockwise

Drink water

Peaches

Sip peppermint tea

Ginger

Exercise

Cut down on salty foods

Pineapple

Asparagus

Garlic

Cucumber

Leeks

177

ACNE

Everyone knows what it's like to wake up, look in the mirror and be greeted by a new friend (or friends) on your face. When we get spots, pimples or acne, it can really impact our confidence. It's really common in your teens and your twenties. Hormonal acne can happen when you're coming up to your period or when on your period.

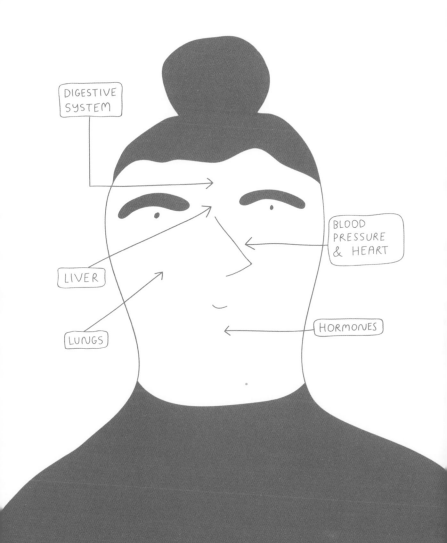

DO

STAY CLEAN

Keep your hands and
phone screen clean

TAKE

Primose oil capsules

EAT GOOD FATS

Avocado, flax oil,
coconut oil & nuts

TREAT

With natural remedies such as tea tree oil, apple cider vinegar, or witch hazel

HEAL SCARS

Use rosehip oil, coconut oil or aloe vera

CHANGE

Your pillowcase regulary

DO NOT

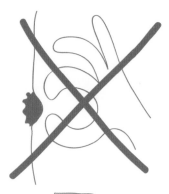

PICK

They <u>will</u>
multiply & scar

OVERUSE SPOT CREAM

These creams can
be very strong

TOUCH

Dirty hands
won't help!

CANCEL YOUR PLANS

EVERYONE gets them so
try not to get too down
and let them stop you
living your life

"Every cycle I get a couple of spots around my mouth. They appear just a day or two before I start bleeding. I've gotten used to this sign now and everytime I get a new friend on my face, I know I better pick up some tampons."

SORE BOOBS

Another common symptom of PMS is sore boobs.
They can feel achy, swollen, tender, denser, lumpy
or just different. So if you want to check for
lumps, it may be a good idea to check a week
after your period. This change is caused by the
decrease in the hormones oestrogen and progesterone.
When your boobs are painful, you may not feel
like exercising or even want to hug anyone.

THESE MAY HELP:
A PERIOD BRA

Make sure you get measured when you are on your
period and get a bra that is comfortable for you.
The majority of bra-owners are bouncing around
with the wrong size. You may want to go without
a wire or for stronger padding as protection against hugs.

MASSAGE

They may need some extra TLC on your period.
It's easy to do, just grab some cream or oil
and go to town.

PAINKILLERS
If all else fails.

LⓋVE
YOUR
BOOBS

DID YOU KNOW?

Most boobs are not symmetrical; they are sisters not twins. In fact everyone has some sort of difference between one boob to another. Some are one or two cup sizes different. During puberty you may notice this more as your body is still growing and can change very quickly in a short space of time. Unfortunately the majority of boobs we see in magazines, on Instagram or on telly, have been altered in some way. Whether it's from surgery, an expensive bra, make-up contouring or photo editing, they are often not their natural boobs! It's important to know this so you don't compare yourself to those bodies. What we see on screen isn't an accurate representation of real bodies.

FOOD

Changing your diet may really help with PMS. Start by picking some of these foods to cut down on and see if you notice any diffence in your PMS:

alcohol

Salt

Sugar

Caffeine

DO NOT SKIP MEALS, instead try to eat balanced meals regularly that include these wholesome foods:

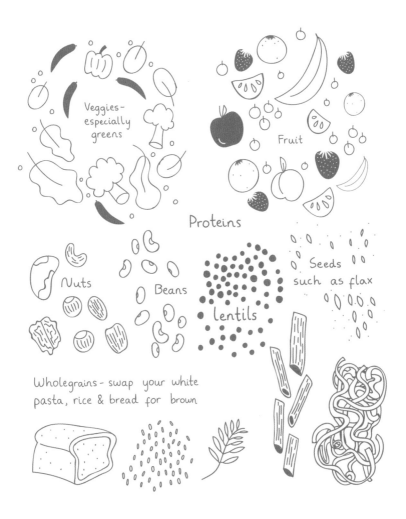

Veggies - especially greens

Fruit

Proteins

Nuts

Beans

Lentils

Seeds such as flax

Wholegrains - swap your white pasta, rice & bread for brown

EXERCISE

Moving your body really does help with the pain, the length of your period and can also lift your mood. Don't underestimate the influence exercise has on the body. When you get your body moving, happy endorphines get released. Just move in a way that feels good to you and the way you enjoy. There's no need to push yourself over the limit.

MOOD CHANGES

When you're due on your period, or actually on it, you might suddenly feel very upset, anxious, annoyed or have low self-esteem. You might find yourself changing clothes 1000 times, crying randomly or snapping at the people around you. This is typical PMS. Try not to be too hard on yourself and let yourself have a big cry.

One thing you can practice is talking to yourself as if talking to a friend. You would never be mean to a friend, so don't be mean to yourself.

MENTAL HEALTH

We all have mental health and it is just as important as physical heath. Working on your mental health can help you fulfil your full potential and live a satisfying life. It can help you think and act rationally and help you through the challenges that life will inevitably throw at you.

If you are not feeling yourself, or are always low, this may be something other than PMS. There are lots of different mental health problems all with different indicators. You don't have to keep all your emotions, feelings and thoughts to yourself. Talking about it with friends, family or a professional is necessary. There is no shame in asking for help, seeing a doctor or taking medication.

WHAT IS MENTAL HEALTH?

"Mental health is a state of well-being in which the individual realises their own potential, can cope with the normal stresses of life, can work productively and fruitfully and are able to make a contribution to their community."
World Health Organization

BASIC HUMAN NEEDS

Sleep

Food

Outside

Connection

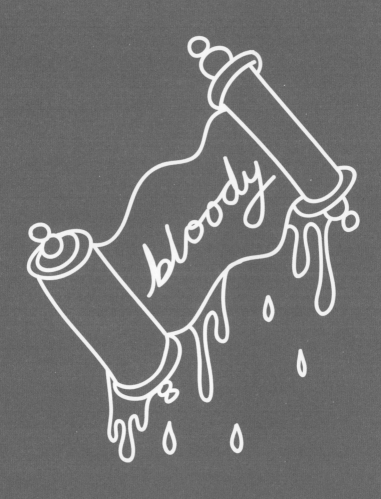

BLOODY HISTORY

WILD, WONDERFUL AND WICKED IDEAS

In all periods of history, people have had the same method of discussing menstruation, which is by not discussing it at all. History was written by white male scribes and their patrons who weren't paying attention to female experiences.

ANCIENT EGYPTIANS, GREEKS & ROMANS

In the past they had to get creative so they used soft papyrus around wood to form a DIY tampon, or made pads out of wool, paper, moss, animal skins or grass.

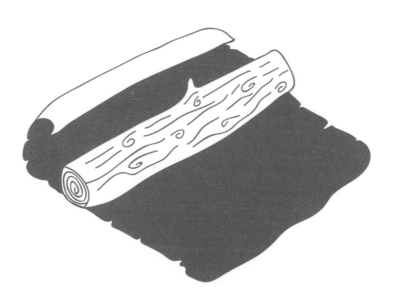

EGYPTIANS

The Egyptians considered a period a cleansing time and some believed that menstrual blood had healing powers. They thought period blood was magical and used it in their spells, medical treatments and even drank it!

ROMANS

The Romans thought menstruating females were basically dark witches.

MEDIEVAL EUROPEANS

Medieval Europeans would hunt down a toad, cook it in a pot and wear the ashes in a pouch near their womb, to ease a heavy flow.

They also thought period blood could cure leprosy, the plague and demonic possession (aka those non-existent evil spirits).

<u>AND FINALLY...</u>

Period blood was thought to be an aphrodisiac (love drug) and some people still believe this to be true.

AFTERWORD

Hi I'm Natalie Byrne, London-based Latina illustrator and the author of *Period*.

In September 2017 I put up my first Instagram post about periods and was really scared. I thought people would find it icky or that it was TMI. Well it turned out that everyone loved it. It became one of my best-liked posts and had the most activity on it. The post got me talking to more and more people about periods and I realised I was not alone in my struggles.

A few months later, I went to the #freeperiods protest organised by Amika George and the girls at Pink Protest and I started to wonder what resources there were for young people about menstruation. I headed to my local library and when I found nothing, I knew that this was something I wanted to change.

Periods are something we are only just beginning to talk about. For centuries we've kept hush-hush about the blood that drips, flows or pours from our bodies. As Isobel Fields said in her wonderful *She Said* podcast:

> *Women still hide the fact that they are menstruating by sticking their tampon in their sleeve when they have to go to the bathroom, (some) men still freak out when someone says period blood. Why in 2018 am I still being told, "Oh she must be on her period", when I express my opinion. I can be loud and angry and passionate and not be menstruating.*

Isobel Fields, "The Act of Menstruation", *She Said,* Episode 1 (2017)

It is with all this in mind that I decided to use my skills as an illustrator to fight against period stigma and menstrual shame and make the book we all wish we'd had.

love Natalie